baby

record book

PULTENEY
PRESS

PULTENEY
PRESS

First published by Pulteney Press in 2008
Copyright © Pulteney Press 2008

ISBN 978-1-78718-691-0
Printed in China

these are the records and keepsakes of

contents

contents

introduction

Childhood is a precious time, full of achievements – that first magical smile, those first tottering steps,

music of those first words. Time rushes past at what seems like a furious rate, and as we delight at each

new milestone reached, we can soon forget the joy we experienced at the last one. But there is a way

to capture forever the wonder of those moments, and that is to record them as they happen –

in words, in pictures and with keepsakes.

In this lovely volume you will find the framework to create your own unique and tangible memory

of your child's first precious year to treasure for the years to come.

The date my mum found out she was expecting me was

_____

My first heatbeat was recorded on

_____

Mum had her first ultrasound scan on

_____

Mum first felt me kick on

_____

Foods my mum craved were

_____

Mum's special memories

_____

ultrasound scan image

special memories

_____
_____
_____
_____
_____
_____

my birthday

I was born on

_____

at   o'clock in the

_____

I was born at

_____

I weighed

_____

I measured   long

_____

My hair is

_____

My eyes are

_____

My most distinguishing features are

_____

I look most like

_____

I was delivered by

_____

here I am!

special memories

_____

_____

_____

_____

_____

_____

My first visitors were

_____

_____

_____

I received cards from

_____

_____

_____

I received gifts from

_____

_____

_____

mementos of my birthday

my birth announcement card

my favourite card

my hospital name tag.

My first name is

_____

_____

It means

_____

It was chosen because

_____

My last name is

_____

My naming ceremony was on

_____

It was held at

_____

and afterwards at

_____

I wore

_____

_____

Special memories of the day

_____

_____

_____

The guests were

_____

_____

_____

_____

_____

My presents were

_____

_____

_____

_____

my naming ceremony invitation

this is me at my naming ceremony

special memories

my family

My mother's name is

_____

My mother's maiden name was

_____

My father's name is

_____

My brothers and sisters are

_____

_____

here she is!

here he is!

my family

special memories

_____

_____

_____

_____

_____

_____

my family tree

grandparents

_____

_____

grandparents

_____

_____

aunts and uncles

_____

_____

_____

parents

_____

_____

aunts and uncles

_____

_____

_____

brothers

_____

_____

me

_____

sisters

_____

_____

my first home

My first home is at

_____

_____

I arrived home on _____ **at** _____ **o'clock**

The weather was

_____

My room is decorated in

_____

my first home

my times of the day

My feeding times are

_____

_____

My sleeping times are

_____

_____

My playtimes are

_____

_____

My grumpy times are

_____

_____

This is the first time that I

Had my first bath

smiled

laughed

lifted my head

slept through the night

recognised my mum

recognised my dad

had my hair cut

bath time!

special memories

_____

_____

_____

_____

_____

_____

This was the first time I

played with my hands

and my feet

held a toy

played peek-a-boo

smiled at my reflection

waved goodbye

clapped my hands

pointed my finger

26

play time!

special memories

_____
_____
_____
_____
_____
_____

My first outing was to

_____

I went with

_____

I first went

in a car _____

on a bus _____

on a train _____

on a boat _____

in an aeroplane _____

28

out and about!

special memories

_____

_____

_____

_____

_____

_____

my favourite things

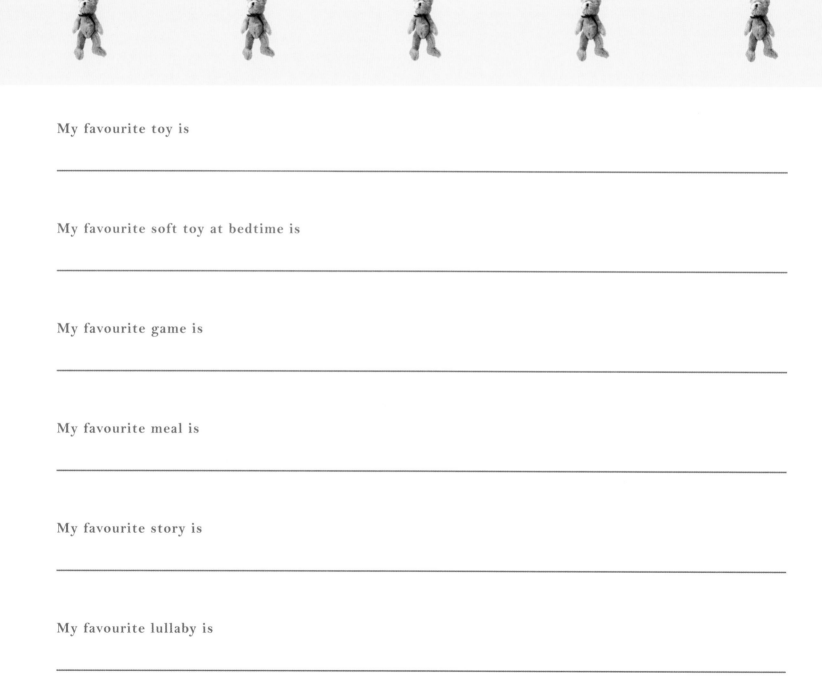

My favourite toy is

_____

My favourite soft toy at bedtime is

_____

My favourite game is

_____

My favourite meal is

_____

My favourite story is

_____

My favourite lullaby is

_____

me with my favourite toy

special memories

_____

_____

_____

_____

_____

_____

my first teeth

This is when my first teeth grew

1 _____

2 _____

3 _____

4 _____

5 _____

6 _____

7 _____

8 _____

I bought my first toothbrush on

_____

My dentist's name is

_____

My first visit was on

_____

32

my first tooth

special memories

_____

_____

_____

_____

_____

_____

My doctor's name is

_____

My nurse's name is

_____

I had my vaccinations for:

_____

_____

_____

on

_____

and

_____

_____

_____

on

and

_____

_____

_____

on

_____

and

pre-school boosters on

_____

Sometimes I was sick.

I had _____

on _____

I had _____

on _____

I had _____

on _____

I had _____

on _____

I had _____

on _____

mealtime

I ate my first solid food on _____

It was _____

I first used a baby cup on _____

I could drink on my own by _____

I first held my spoon on _____

I first fed myself on _____

My favourite foods are _____

I do not like _____

I stopped bottle feeds when I was _____

mealtime!

special memories

_____

_____

_____

_____

_____

_____

my growth chart

Length	Weight	Foot Size	Length	Weight	Foot Size
At 1 month:	♡	♡	At 7 months:	♡	♡
At 2 months:	♡	♡	At 8 months:	♡	♡
At 3 months:	♡	♡	At 9 months:	♡	♡
At 4 months:	♡	♡	At 10 months:	♡	♡
At 5 months:	♡	♡	At 11 months:	♡	♡
At 6 months:	♡	♡	At 12 months:	♡	♡

This is a print of my hands and feet

My first birthday party was at

_____

Mum and dad gave me

_____

My other presents were

from
_____

from
_____

from
_____

from
_____

My cake was

_____

My best friend is

_____

My favourite games were

_____

_____

my first birthday

special memories

_____

_____

_____

_____

_____

_____

I first rolled over ...

from front to back on _____

from back to front on _____

I first crawled on _____

I first stood with help on _____

and on my own on _____

My first sit-and-ride toy is _____

this is me crawling

this is me standing up

43

toddler group

I started toddler group on

_____

My best friend is

_____

The toys I like are

_____

_____

_____

My favourite toy is

_____

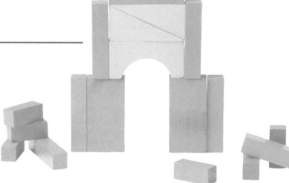

here I am with my friends

special memories

_____

_____

_____

_____

_____

_____

my first christmas

On my first Christmas I was _____ **months old**

I spent Christmas at

_____

with

_____

_____

_____

For Christmas lunch I ate

_____

Santa Claus brought me

_____

_____

_____

_____

46

my first christmas

special memories

_____

_____

_____

_____

_____

_____

my first holiday

For my first holiday I went to

_____

with

_____

We travelled by

_____

We stayed at

_____

What I liked best was

_____

_____

What I did not like was

_____

_____

here I am on holiday!

special memories

_____

_____

_____

_____

_____

_____

The first sounds I made were

_____

When I was _____ months old

_____

my first words were

_____

I spoke to

_____

I soon learned to say

_____

_____

My favourite nursery rhymes are

_____

_____

_____

_____

My favourite songs are

_____

_____

_____

_____

My favourite stories are

_____

_____

_____

_____

I took my first steps on

_____

I was helped by

_____

I walked on my own on

_____

when I took _____ steps

I am good at walking, now I am

_____

me walking!

I learned to climb down the stairs when I was

_____

and up the stairs when I was

_____

Now I am _____ I have my first pair of shoes.

They are size _____

I first ran when I was

_____

I learned to jump when I was

_____

me running!

My second birthday party was at

_____

My presents were

_____ from

_____ from

_____ from

_____ from

_____ from

_____ from

_____ from

_____ from

_____ from

_____ from

_____ from

_____ from

my cake

54

me on my second birthday

Height

Weight

Shoe size

special memories

a print of my hands age two

a print of my feet age two

Things I like

_____

_____

_____

Things I don't like

_____

_____

_____

Special memories

_____

_____

_____

_____

_____

doing something I like

learning more and more

This is when I learned to:

skip

_____

kick a ball

_____

throw a ball

_____

catch a ball

_____

ride a bike

_____

me playing

I started playgroup on

_____

_____

People who care for me at playgroup are

_____

_____

My best friend is

_____

I like to

_____

_____

I do not like to

_____

at playgroup

special memories

_____
_____
_____
_____
_____
_____

my third birthday

My third birthday party was at

_____

My presents were

_____	from
_____	from
_____	from
_____	from
_____	from
_____	from
_____	from
_____	from
_____	from
_____	from
_____	from
_____	from

my cake

me on my third birthday

Height _____

Weight _____

Shoe size _____

special memories

_____

_____

_____

a print of my hands age three

a print of my feet age three

pictures of my family

_____   _____   _____

_____   _____   _____

pictures of my family

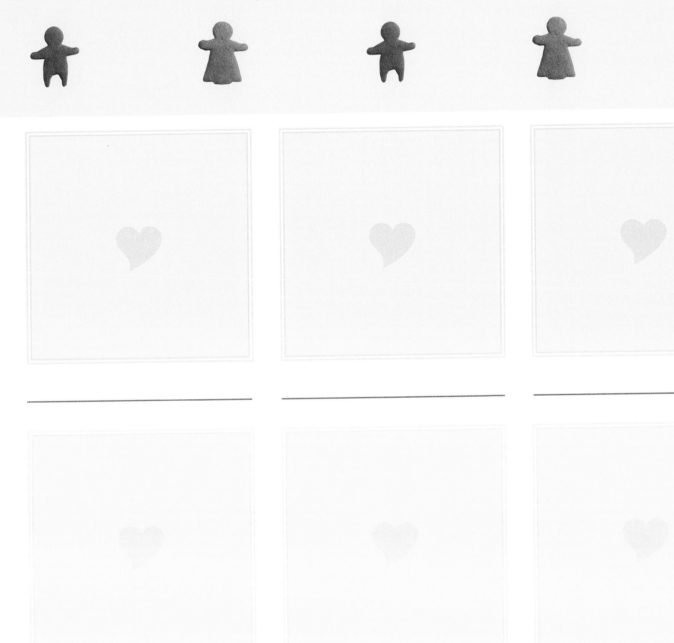

My fourth birthday party was at

_____

My presents were

_____	from _____
_____	from _____
_____	from _____
_____	from _____
_____	from _____
_____	from _____
_____	from _____
_____	from _____
_____	from _____
_____	from _____
_____	from _____
_____	from _____

my cake

me on my fourth birthday

Height _____

Weight _____

Shoe size _____

special memories

_____

_____

_____

Things I like

_____
_____
_____
_____

Things I don't like

_____
_____
_____
_____

Things I have learned to do

_____
_____
_____
_____

This is me when I was _____ years and _____ months old. _____

I was _____ tall and I weighed _____

Picture

look at me now!

71